With a grateful heart, I dedicate this book
to those who encouraged me to never give
up and to continue writing this poem:
Mom, Dad, Conrad, Webb, and Sheila.

I love you all for pushing me to do the work
assigned to me by the Lord Jesus–
the work of telling others the Good News
about the wonderful grace of God.
(Acts 20:24)

'Twas the Night That Began Christmas

by Catherine Conrad Waters
Illustrated by Bill McCracken

C. Waters 2019

© 2018 Catherine Conrad Waters
catherinewaters.com
Second Printing ©2019

Published by SBA Books
PO BOX 3019 · Daphne, AL 36526
sbabooks.com

'Twas the night before Christmas
and all through the town,
not a room was available,
not one could be found.

But an innkeeper provided
a stable to use;
Mary with child...
how could Joseph refuse?

The cattle and sheep
settled in for some sleep;
not a sound could be heard
not even a peep.

This was a night filled with peace
and great joy,
as Mary and Joseph
awaited their boy.

When up in the sky
there arose such a star,
that Wise Men who saw it
came from afar.

They wanted to see
this newborn King,
and present Him with gifts
they longed to bring.

The shepherds were watching
their flocks by night;
when an angel said,
"Come behold a great sight!

You'll find a babe
in swaddling clothes,
laid in a manger~
the plan God chose."

Suddenly there shown
a multitude of hosts;
singing praises to God
and the Holy Ghost.

Then what to their
wondering eyes should appear,
but a tiny baby sent
from heaven- to here!

More rapid than eagles,
Jesus grew to a man,
and chose His disciples
according to plan;

First Peter! Then Philip!
Now Thomas and Andrew!

Next James and Simon,
then John and Bartholomew!

Thaddaeus and Judas,
and then to Matthew.
Now just one more James, because
there were two!

To the top of the hill!

To the top of the mount!

Now teach The Way! Preach The Way!

Preach to them all!

15

So up on the mountain
He taught each command,
using parables to tell,
truths hard to understand.

He said that heaven is
the place to store treasure,
and forgiveness of others
should come without measure.

And then, in a moment,
they heard Jesus say,
"Look up to the Father, and
here's how to pray."

Then He spoke
each word so lovingly;
"Our Father in Heaven,
hallowed be..."

18

His life how it shines;

for He is the True Light,

the beacon of hope,

making everything right.

The Healer of sick;

the Forgiver of all;

the Bread of Life to

those heeding His call.

The One Good Shepherd,

who loves us and cares.

The Resurrector for those

who love Him, He spares.

He is the Deliverer,

the Great I AM;

the One God sent,

the Sacrifice- the Lamb.

He made the deaf to hear
and the blind to see,
and forgave people's sins,
setting all of us free.

But as hate arose,
people yelled, "Crucify!"
And God allowed it,
though some wondered why.

He spoke not a word,
and was nailed to the cross.
For all of our sins,
He alone paid the cost.

How could anyone know
the plan from above,
was to conquer our death,
and show us His love.

He created the heavens
and all of the Earth.

He's the One who gives life
its meaning and worth.

Salvation will not come
by the good works you do,
but it is by His Spirit,
dwelling in you.

We must pray to be filled
with God's Holy Love,
it gives Eternal Life
in Heaven above.

Oh what a glorious
sight we will see,
when Christ Jesus returns,
our Savior is He.

God's Word tells us...

In the beginning was the Word, and the Word was with God, and the Word was God. (John 1:1) ... And the Word became flesh and dwelt among us, and we beheld His glory, as of the only Begotten Son of God, full of grace and truth. (John 1:14)

Therefore the Lord himself will give you a sign: The virgin will conceive and give birth to a son, and will call him Immanuel. (Isaiah 7:14)

For if you forgive other people when they sin against you, your heavenly Father will also forgive you. (Matthew 6:14)

For God so loved the world that He gave His one and only Son, that whoever believes in Him shall not perish, but have eternal life. (John 3:16)

Jesus answered, "I am the way and the truth and the life. No one comes to the Father except through me. (John 14:6)

For it is by grace you have been saved, through faith ~ and this is not from yourselves, it is the gift of God ~ not by works, so that no one can boast. (Ephesians 2:8-9)

In the beginning God created the heavens and the earth. (Genesis 1:1)

So Christ was sacrificed once to take away the sins of many; and He will appear a second time, not to bear sin, but to bring salvation to those who are waiting for Him. (Hebrews 9:28)

Catherine Waters lives in Vestavia Hills, AL with her son, Conrad. She was raised by a loving Christian family, since her birth. Catherine's faith in Jesus led her to write this book in hopes of others coming to know Christ as their Lord and Savior.